LIFE IS LIKE A BAG OF NOISY, STRUGGLING ROOSTERS.

IT IS ENTRUSTED TO US BUT IT IS DIFFICULT TO HOLD.

SOMETIMES WE LOSE OUR GRIP AND THE ROOSTERS ESCAPE

THEY DISPERSE IN A WILD PANIC.....

....AND FOOLISHLY WE SPEND THE REST OF OUR DAYS TRYING TO ROUND THEM UP.

WORSE STILL: AS WE SEARCH WE DRAG THE EMPTY SACK BEHIND US AND OBLITERATE OUR FOOTSTEPS....

A Bag of Roosters

BY

Michael Leunig

ANGUS & ROBERTSON PUBLISHERS

Unit 4, Eden Park, 31 Waterloo Road,
North Ryde, NSW, Australia 2113;
94 Newton Road, Auckland 1,
New Zealand; and
16 Golden Square, London W1R 4BN,
United Kingdom

First published in Australia
by Angus & Robertson Publishers in 1983
First published in the United Kingdom
by Angus & Robertson (UK) Ltd in 1984
Reprinted 1986, 1989

National Library of Australia
Cataloguing-in-publication data.

Leunig, Michael.
A bag of roosters.

ISBN 0 207 14830 9.

1. Australian wit and humor, pictorial.
2. Caricatures and cartoons — Australia.
I. Title.

741.5'994

Printed in Hong Kong

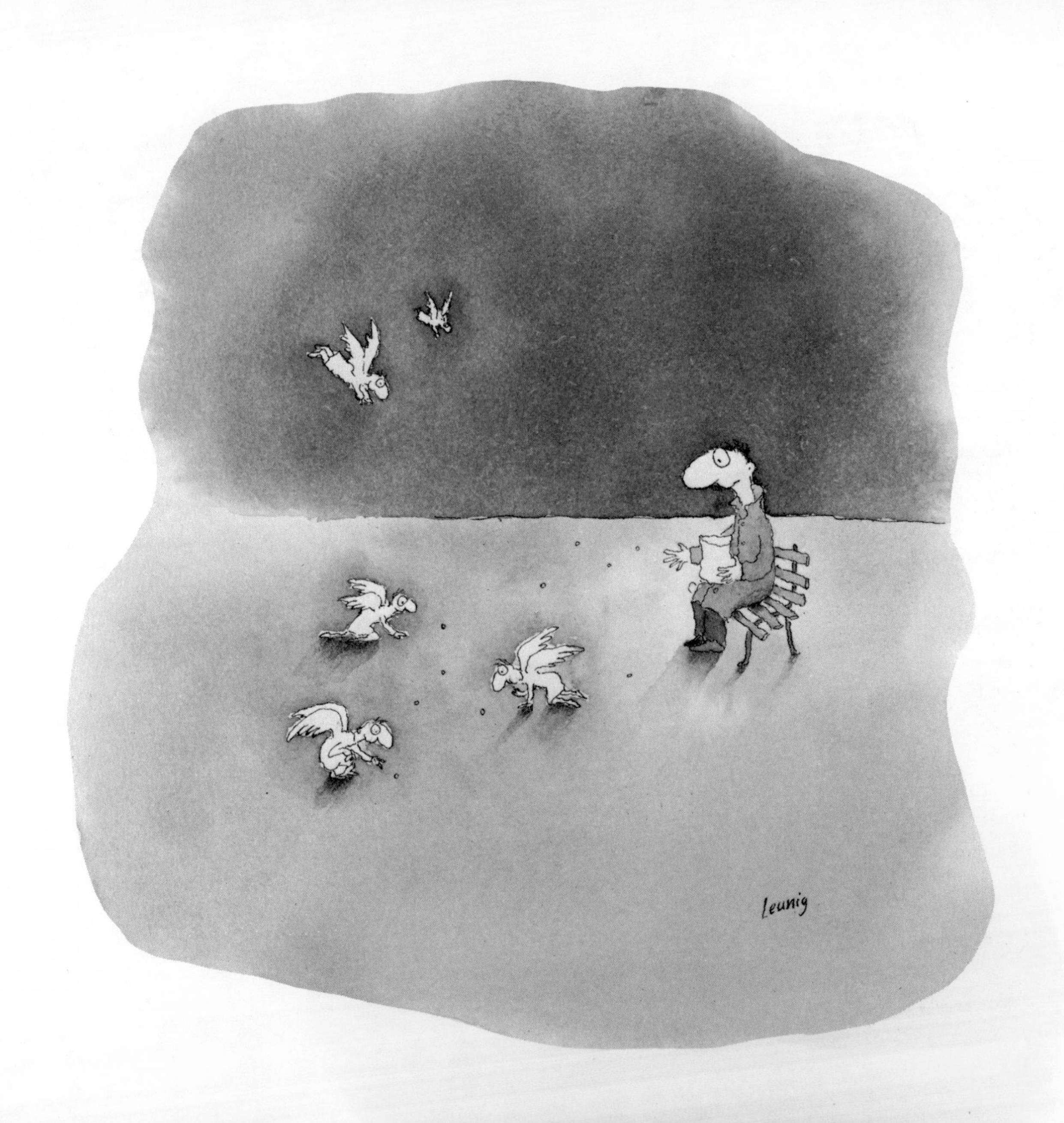
Leunig

Leunig

Leunig

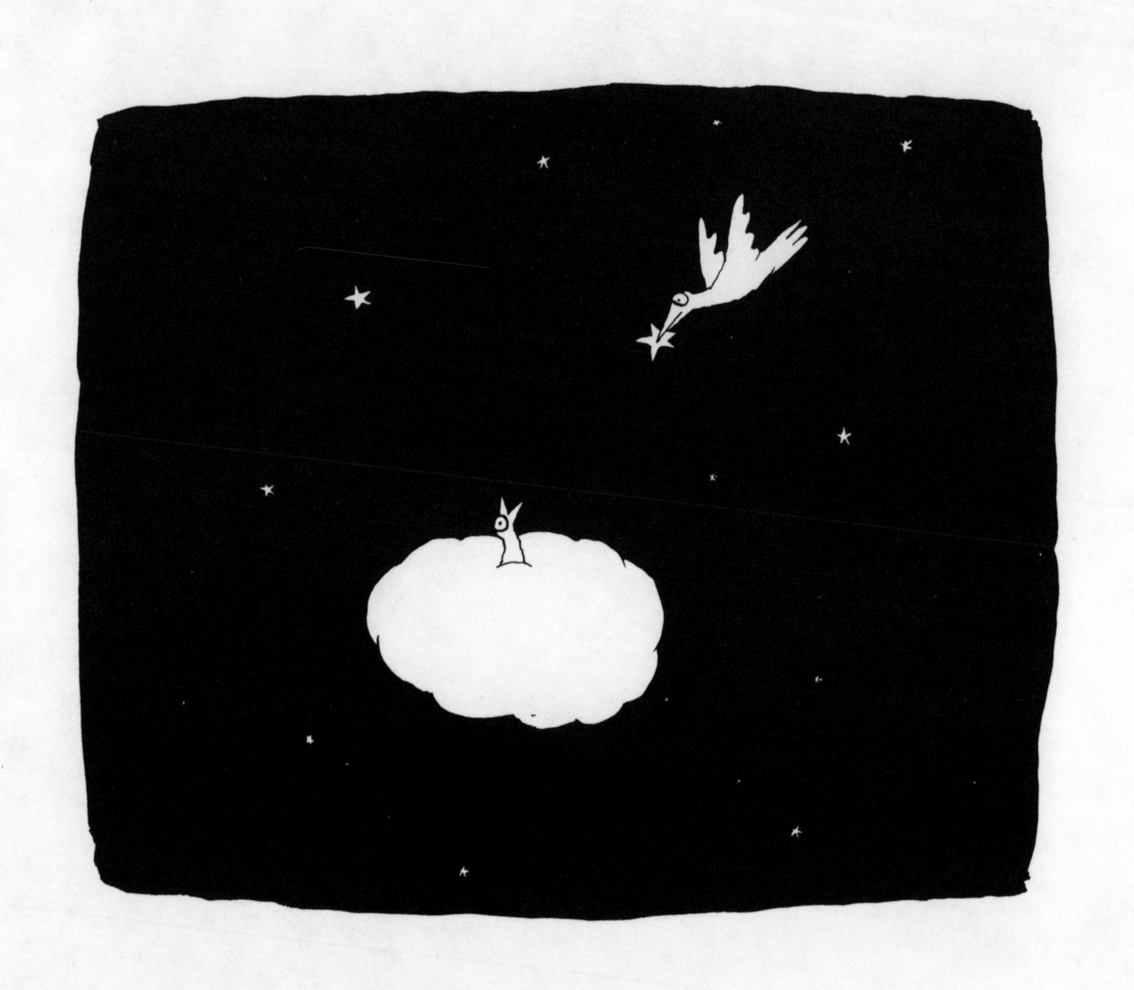

Leunig

BEEN THERE...
DONE THAT..

TOO HARD
BASKET

UHH...!
H...H... WHO ARE YOU ? WHAT ARE YOU DOING TO MY FACE...?
I AM THE DETERIORATING ANGEL.... I VISIT ONCE A WEEK FOR THE REST OF YOUR LIFE..

I'm putting a few wrinkles in while you sleep.... greying out a few hairs... dulling the light in the eyes a little..

I'm a gradual angel really... and I always polish your mirror after every visit..

Leunig

CHALET BAR
SWINGLES DISCO INFERNO
SLAM
Leunig

ENEMY LEAFLETS FALL FROM ABOVE...

"give up... you are beaten.... you will never make sense of it alone... stop trying now."

"accept it... you are outnumbered.... overwhelmed... surrounded. come and join us."

"you are not a hero... there is no glory in your cause... your fight is worthless.."

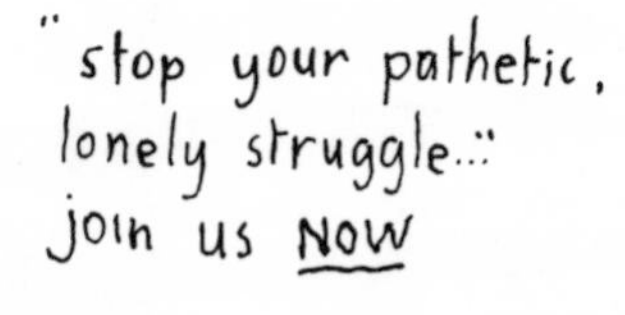

"stop your pathetic, lonely struggle..." join us NOW

"turn to page 6 for our great television guide... sport, page 32 politics, page 10 modern living, page 14"

THIS CITY IS NUCLEAR FREE

THIS STREET IS NUCLEAR FREE

THIS HOUSE IS NUCLEAR FREE

THIS IS A NUCLEAR FREE BED

Leunig

SECURITY
PASS

I'M HOMESICK...
I YEARN... I PINE..
I WANT TO GO
HOME....

WHAT ARE YOU
SAYING....?
THIS IS YOUR
HOME..

THERE'S YOUR UNDERPANTS
ON THE FLOOR...
YOUR CAR IN THE DRIVE...

YOUR DISHES IN THE SINK...
YOUR COCKATOO IN ITS' CAGE...

HERE IS YOUR CITY....
THERE ARE YOUR PEOPLE...
THIS IS YOUR LIFE...

I WANT
TO GO
HOME..

Leunig

Leunig

SO... you believe in this do you..?
...well just watch

YOU SEE.... COMPLETELY HOLLOW..!

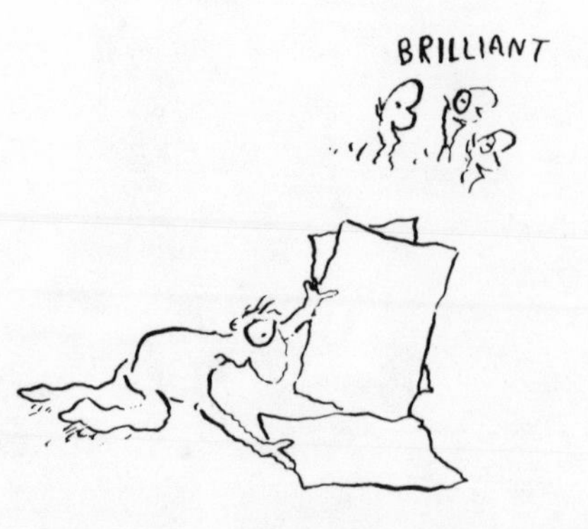
BRILLIANT

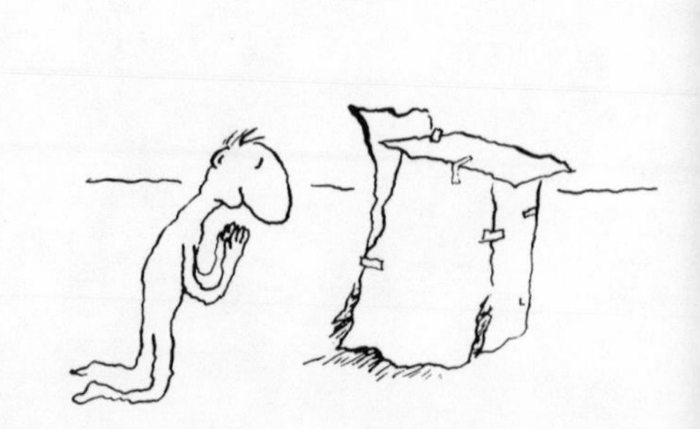

Leunig

SHOULD CHILDREN BELIEVE IN SANTA....? SHOULD SANTA BELIEVE IN CHILDREN...?

DOES CHILDHOOD REALLY EXIST OR IS IT JUST AN OLD CHRISTMAS LEGEND....?

AND IF IT EXISTS; IS IT INHABITED BY ACTUAL CHILDREN..? INNOCENT, HOPEFUL CHILDREN...?

TRUSTING BELIEVERS..... SAVIOURS AND RENEWERS... THE GREATEST LOVERS... THE SWEETEST DREAMERS..?

ONE PERSON, SANTA CLAUS, STILL BELIEVES IN ALL THESE THINGS AND EACH CHRISTMAS NIGHT HE GOES OUT SEARCHING FOR AS MANY SUCH CHILDREN AS HE CAN FIND

HE TIP-TOES INTO THEIR HOMES JUST FOR THE LOVE OF SEEING THEM SLEEPING.
HE IS SO GRATEFUL FOR THEIR EXISTENCE THAT HE LEAVES GIFTS

OCCASIONALLY EVEN SANTA HAS HIS DOUBTS. TO HIM IT SOMETIMES ALL SEEMS TOO GOOD TO BE TRUE.

OVERLOOKING MY LIFE SO FAR

In my life I had accumulated many things in my head...... TOO MANY THINGS...!

Memories, tunes, facts, fears, visions, loves... etc. etc... as many as possible

In a fertile mind such things will interbreed. mongrel visions are born .... hybrid memories.... inbred, idiot love.... It gets very CONFUSING

I decided it was time for a good cleanup so I emptied it all out of my head and pushed it up in a big heap to sort it out.

There it was.... everything that was me, all in a big jumbled heap. I walked around it. What a mess...!

Then suddenly I saw it in silhouette and realized what it was.... IT WAS A HEAP.... A SIMPLE HEAP...! you don't sort it out.. you climb it... you climb it because it is there...

Excitedly I clambered to the summit and raised a flag. I was now looking beyond everything that I knew.

LIFE'S RICH
AND VARIED
TAPESTRY
GAUZE
BANDAGE

Leunig

One sunny day you look down and there it is at your feet... a tiny piece of gold.

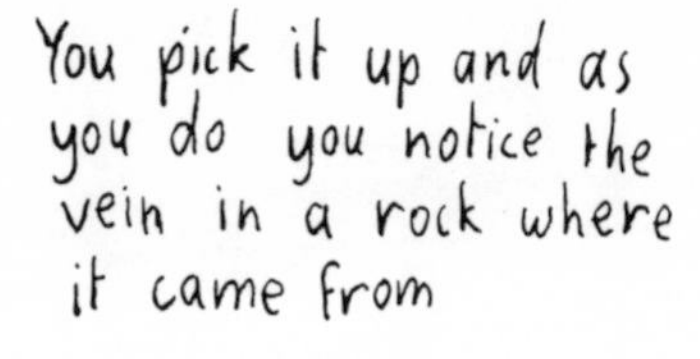

You pick it up and as you do you notice the vein in a rock where it came from

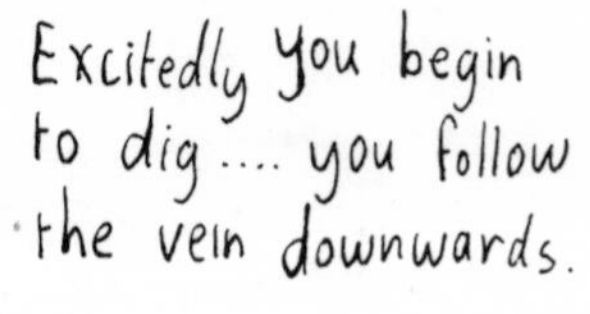

Excitedly you begin to dig.... you follow the vein downwards.

Down, down.... away from the sun... you work earnestly and the years pass.

Deeper you follow the lead. Smashing at the rock face.... propping the tunnel... exhausting yourself.

You begin to fear a cave-in and by now it is too dark to see the gold.

All you can do is feel its weight in your hands.

Back on the surface is another beautiful sunny day.... the same as it ever was.

The Museum of Manners.

CHAPTER FIVE OF MY BIOGRAPHY

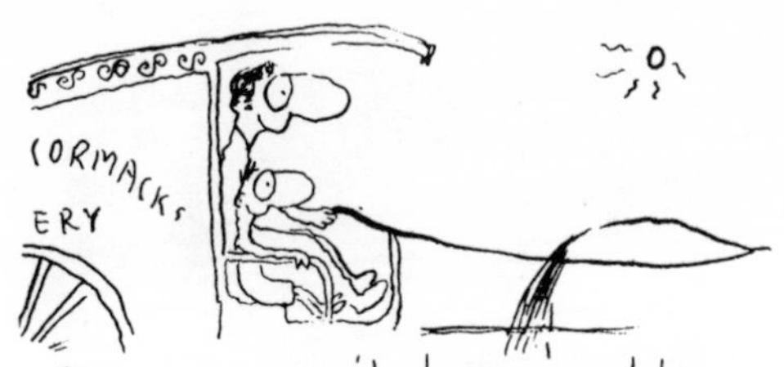

My interest in the human mind began on a warm afternoon in 1952. After lunching at home I had returned to school on the bakers' cart to find the playground in a state of high excitement.

Robert Barr had split his head on the log swing. They said you could actually see his brain and I had missed the whole thing

I was shown a small bloodstain on the gravel behind the incinerator

I had missed a wonderful and chilling insight. I had missed Robert Barr's live brain... his actual mind where all his thinking happened ...... his very soul which would one day find its way to heaven or hell

So profound and bitter was my frustration... so thrilling my curiosity that I dedicated my life there and then to the miserable pursuit of peeping into the human soul and reporting my observations.

Fate is wild. Had I not gone home for lunch... had I stayed and glimpsed Robert Barr's brain as he lay whimpering on the gravel I could have gone on to become a drunk.... a womaniser and quite possibly the Prime Minister of AUSTRALIA.

Leunig

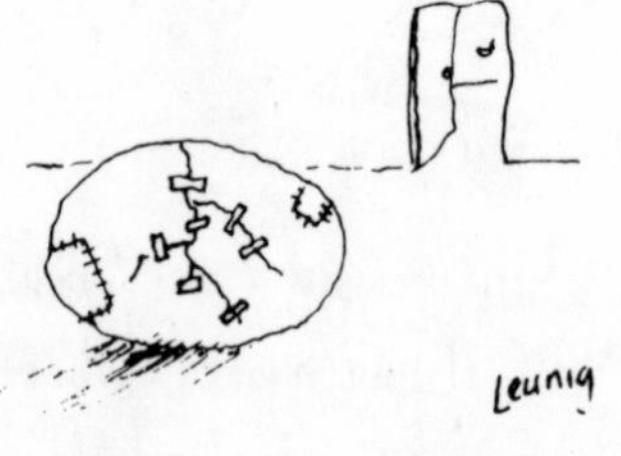
Leunig

Oh give me a home where the buffalo roam, Where the deer and the antelope play. . .

VACANCY FOR BLOWFLY CATCHER. MUST HAVE BACHELOR OF ARTS

PEST CONTROL Co.
B.A.

B.A.
SWAT

The awful party.

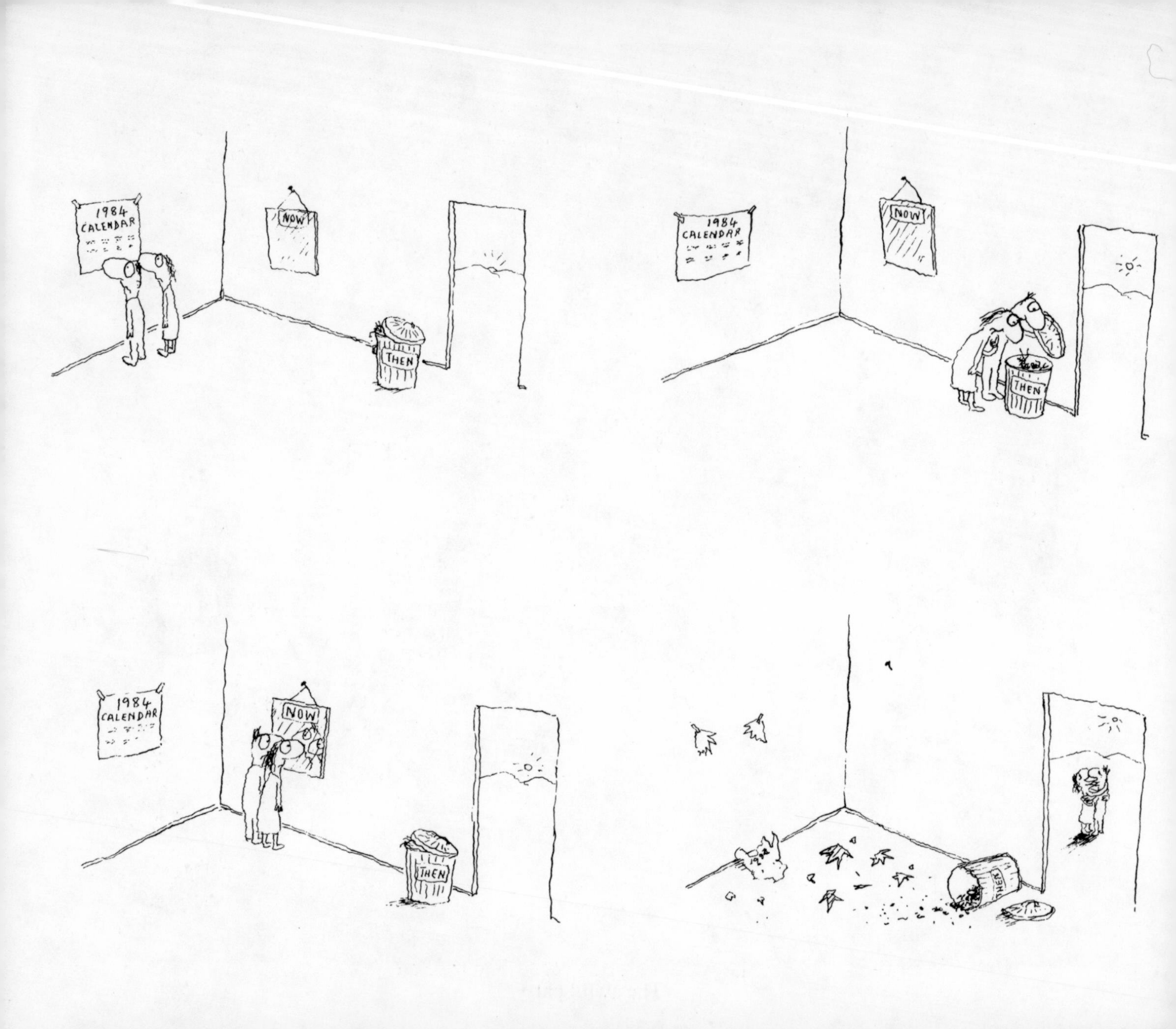
1984
CALENDAR
NOW
THEN
1984
CALENDAR
NOW
THEN
1984
CALENDAR
NOW
THEN
THEN

The Australian **Iron Man** Championship.

A FABLE

Two thousand feet above Scotland a tail gunner in a crippled British bomber tears off his burning parachute and clothes and leaps in panic from the airborne inferno...

Plummeting naked through the night he thinks he is about to die...

He lands on a deep drift of powdery snow which has settled on some fine spruce branches.

This cushions his fall and he drops through it onto a shingle roof which collapses under him

And finally he lands safely and softly on a thick, warm eiderdown on a large bed beside a beautiful woman in a nightgown.

At that moment the womans husband enters the room with cup of steaming cocoa and in a sudden jealous rage flings the scalding beverage over the naked airman.

The gunner is reunited with his crew in the burns ward of a London hospital.

MORAL

GOD PUNISHES THOSE WHO SURVIVE TOO EXTRAVAGANTLY

YOU HAVE BEEN WARNED...!

Leunig

Simpson and his Rooster.

GOLD...
GOLD...

GOLD...!
IT'S A SAUSAGE. ROLL....

Leunig

Leunig

HOWDY
AND
WELCOME

GLIMPSES OF CURLY FLAT

MR. CURLY'S HOME TOWN

The town of Curly Flat.

In Curly Flat unforeseen circumstances are celebrated . . .
accidents bring out the best in people.

In Curly Flat people often change direction and turn off roads to free themselves from the expected way ahead.
The Tyranny of the Inevitable.

By the shores of Lake Lacuna.

Tourists unwind in the mysterious whirlpools of Lake Lacuna.

The vineyard at Curly Flat.
The locals have never bothered to describe the taste or construction of their wines but after drinking a couple of glasses they are inclined to become very eloquent in describing the way it makes them feel.

A whirlwind passes through the Curly Flat flower farm.
From the great spiralling nebulae of the heavens to the delicate tendrils of the vine, God moves in curly ways.

A birthday surprise.
Mr Curly wakes in amazement to find an old friend in his bed.

The Curly Flat Botanical Gardens contain the largest collection of curly plants in the world. Included are the curly palm *(Phoenix whirl)*, the twisted oak *(Quercus circulae)* and the spinning pine *(Pinus concentrus)*.

The poultry farm at Curly Flat.

The Orchestra of Horns rehearsing.

"Gone, gone, gone . . ." The cry goes up in a darkened hall, climaxing the amazing Ceremony of the Muffled Oar. The citizens of Curly Flat gather annually in a ritual celebration of the mysteries and joys of the "unscheduled exit", the most beloved of the social arts.

I am on my death bed; cold and alone in a dim, sordid room. Through the window I see the city in a greyish. yellow smoke haze. A rocket streaks across the evening sky. Everything is lost.

Suddenly some type of angel is present and tells me I can be granted a few minutes of my past to live over again... I am asked to choose which few minutes I want

Without thinking I say I would dearly love any few minutes ... anything at all would be precious.

And suddenly I am standing in a paddock of dry grass in the country. The sky is deep blue ... the sun glitters through the leaves of a large red gum. It is late afternoon. There are two children ... ... a pond ... magpies sing. I am young.

How precious .... I am standing in a simple and wonderful vision ... ecstatic .. .. tranquil. If only I had loved my entire life as I loved these few minutes reprieve from death.

Just then the sun flashed in my eyes and it dawned on me. This is no reprieve ..... THIS IS MY LIFE. These trees ..... these magpies ..... this sunlight ..... this rusty old bed in the pond.

SING
DAMN YOU....
SING

THE WORLD IS GOING
MAD.... DON'T LET
ME DOWN....
PLEASE....
SING....
SING

YOU
SWINE

SING
SING
SING
YOU
ROTTEN
SWINE
SING..!!

Leunig

DEAR FRIENDS
LIFE IS MUCH
TOO CONFUSING
I MUST END IT.
HELLO
x x x
Leunig

YOU ARE CRUISING TO A MYSTERY DESTINATION. MID OCEAN.... NIGHT TIME. YOU ATTEND A GLITTERING OCCASION IN THE BALLROOM.

YOU NOTICE A WOMAN WHO IS SO RARE AND BEAUTIFUL TO YOU THAT YOU GROW WEAK.... LONELY... ECSTATIC. SHE DANCES WITH THE CAPTAIN AND SOME OFFICERS

DAZED WITH A STRANGE RESIGNATION. YOU MOVE OUT TO THE RAIL AND DROP LIMPLY OVERBOARD. YOU SWIM AWAY FROM THE SHIP TO WONDER AT IT ALL FROM AFAR.

IN THE BLACKNESS A SHARK BUMPS INTO YOUR LEG AND FROM A MILE ACROSS THE WATER YOU HEAR MUSIC, LAUGHTER.... THE CLINK OF GLASSES. YOU SEE THE TWINKLING LIGHTS. THE OCEAN FLOOR IS A THOUSAND FATHOMS BENEATH YOU. YOU FEEL MYSTICAL..... UNAFRAID.

THEN YOU SWIM BACK TO THE SHIP AND ONLY JUST MAKING IT YOU CLAMBER UP A ROPE.... EXHAUSTED. THE WOMAN IS ON THE DECK.... ALONE. SHE HAS BEEN SEARCHING FOR YOU, WORRYING FOR YOU. SHE HELPS YOU OVER THE RAIL. SHE WARMS YOU IN HER ARMS. A TEAR OF RELIEF ON HER CHEEK, SHE KISSES YOU...

YOU NEARLY FAINT WITH JOY. A CLOCK STRIKES TWELVE. THE SHIP TURNS INTO A LIVE SHEEP TRANSPORT. YOU ARE KISSING A SHEEP...! YOU ARE BOUND FOR LIBYA. EVERYTHING SMELLS.

NO WONDER IT'S
UNCOMFORTABLE....
IT'S EMPTY...!

DROUGHT ADVICE FOR THE MAN ON THE LAND.

SO YOU'VE HAD ENOUGH OF THE DROUGHT. THE FARM IS BLOWING AWAY, THE GARDEN'S DEAD AND EVERYTHING LOOKS BLOODY AWFUL.

YOU WANT RELIEF .... HERE'S WHAT TO DO. FIRSTLY, DRINK ONE BOTTLE OF BEER....... THEN GRAB A LONG, WHIPPY STICK OFF A DEAD SHRUB IN THE GARDEN.

NOW GO TO THE FOWL YARD AND CORNER THE ROOSTER....... .... THEN....

....WHIP HIM...! THAT'S RIGHT.... WHIP THE ROOSTER... FLY INTO HIM...! GO ON.... GO LIKE STINK! WHIP HIM HARD.

HARDER... HARDER...! WHIP HIM.... IT'S ALL HIS BLOODY FAULT... get into him.... go on.. WHIP THE MONGREL... whip him...

N.B. ROOSTER WHIPPING IS A TRADITIONAL AUSTRALIAN DROUGHT REMEDY BUT IS NOT CONDONED BY ANIMAL LIBERATION OR THE R.S.P.C.A.

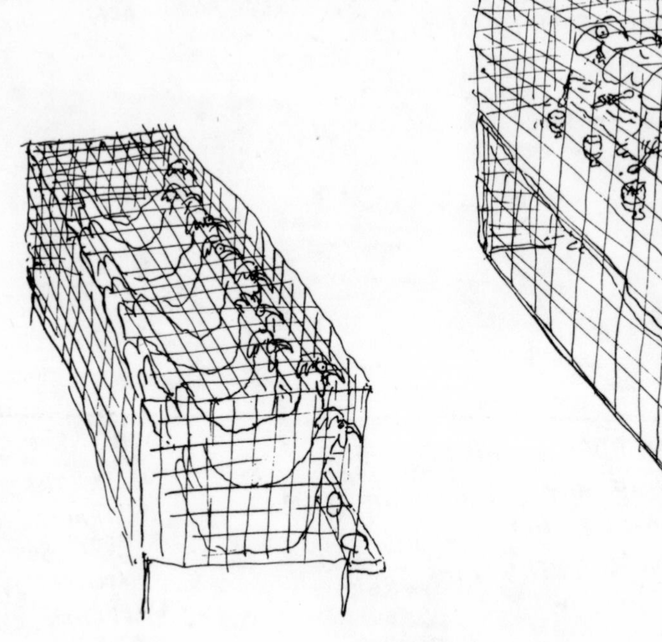
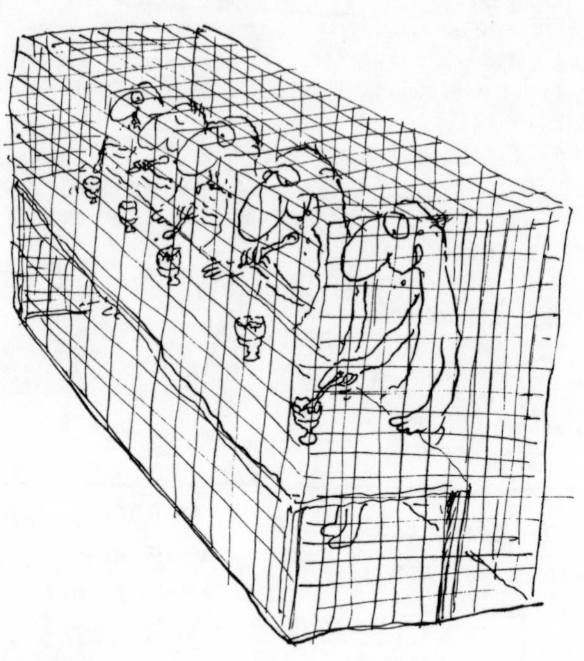

leunig

BAMBO
CAFE
Leunig

COLLIE
FOXIE

SO YOU'VE LOST YOUR JOB....
HEY...!
FORGET THE BLUES...
IT'S CUP EVE

YAY YAY YAIRRR...!
IT'S MELBOURNE CUP TIME...
DO THE TWIST.

HEY
HEY
HEY...
DO THE SHAKE

IT'S CUP EVE BABY...
GO FOR IT...
WORK OUT NOW....!!

CUP FEVER BABY..
GET DOWN AND
WHIP IT... HEY
...wild thing... DIG IT..

FAR OUT.....
SHAKE IT
SHAKE IT
SHAKE IT
WOOOOOOOOO!

Leunig

HIS + HER CONTRACEPTIVE
PACK

AH WELL... suppose I better get ready and go out and pull a job...

HOW DO I LOOK...?

TOTALLY, WONDERFULLY EVIL AND CORRUPT

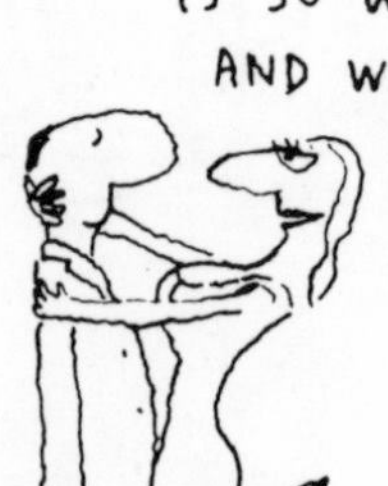
YOUR COLLAR IS SO WHITE AND WICKED...

I'M HOT FOR YOU LOUIE...

SAVE IT FOR LATER KID....

GOOD LUCK LOUIE...
Leunig

What does it mean when a man unearths an ancient urn but in doing so buries his thermos flask?

HUMAN OVA VEHICLE
LIVE HUMAN SPERM TRANSPORT
MONASH UNIVERSITY DEPT OF PHILOSOPHY

Leunig

SOME ENCHANTED EVENING

ATMOSPHERE

DO YOU HAVE A BOOKING MADAM?
WELL ACTUALLY NO.... I JUST WANTED TO LOOK AROUND THE OLD PLACE...
DINERS CLUB
BANKCARD
I WAS BORN HERE... SEVENTY YEARS AGO, RIGHT IN THIS ROOM... IT WAS THE FRONT BEDROOM THEN

AND THIS WAS THE LOUNGE ROOM WHERE DAD DIED.. RIGHT THERE HE SAID HE WAS TIRED...
HE JUST LAY DOWN AND DIED RIGHT THERE IN THAT SPOT
I'LL NEVER FORGET IT.. WE THOUGHT HE WAS ASLEEP... HE WAS SMILING... WHAT A LOVELY WAY TO GO..
FORGIVE ME... THERE ARE SO MANY MEMORIES FOR ME HERE.... EVEN THOUGH YOU'VE CHANGED IT.....
PONT NEUF FRENCH CUISINE
IT STILL HAS A WONDERFUL ATMOSPHERE
Leunig

GRACE = MC^2

I APPRECIATE YOU ACCEPTING ME INTO HEAVEN BUT....

.... I FEEL SO GUILTY HERE WITH ALL THOSE POOR, DAMNED BEGGARS DOWN THERE ....

... SUFFERING IN HELL. IT DOESN'T SEEM RIGHT. I'D RATHER SHARE THEIR BURDEN.
PLEASE LET ME GO TO HELL TO BE WITH MY PEOPLE.

SUCH COMPASSION...!
YOU ARE TRULY VIRTUOUS.

I HEREBY PROMOTE YOU TO THE HIGHEST LEVEL OF PARADISE

HAVE A GOOD TIME...

Leunig

HELP ME
I'M A
LATERAL
THINKER
Leunig

Leunig

AHHH.. SUMMER! THE MUNICIPAL POOL. THE DIVING BOARD AND THE MEANING OF LIFE.

YOUR TURN HAS COME, YOU HAVE CLIMBED THE LADDER.. YOU WILL FLY ACROSS THE SUN.

BENEATH YOU WAITS THE POOL OF LIFE AND TRUTH WHERE ALL SOULS MUST STRUGGLE TO STAY AFLOAT

YOUR FLIGHT MUST LAST AS LONG AS POSSIBLE IT MUST BE ORIGINAL, POWERFUL, ENTERTAINING, INSPIRING AND STYLISH.

YOU MUST ENTER THE POOL WITH A MIGHTY SPLASH. YOU MUST CAUSE A TIDAL WAVE.

YOU ARE ABOUT TO FLY BUT SOMEBODY JUMPS ON THE MIDDLE OF THE BOARD BEHIND YOU

YOU SLIP AND FALL YOU CATCH HOLD OF THE BOARD. SOMEBODY STANDS ON YOUR FINGERS YOU LOSE YOUR GRIP

YOU DROP.. IT IS A "PIN" DIVE. THERE IS NO SPLASH... THE LAST THING YOU HEAR BEFORE GOING UNDER IS LAUGHTER

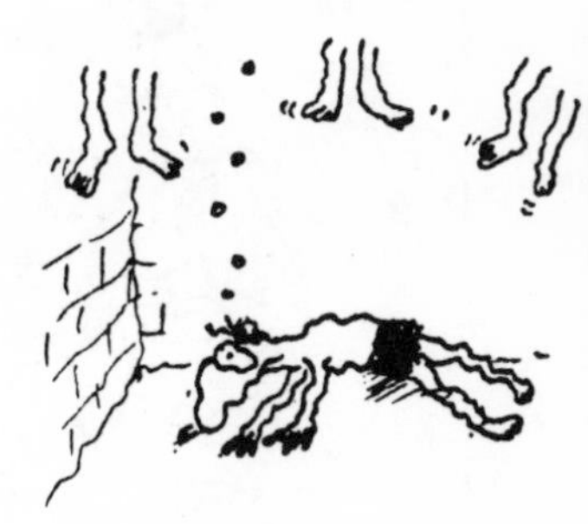

AT THE BOTTOM OF THE POOL YOU GRASP THE MEANING OF LIFE BUT WEEPING IS IMPOSSIBLE UNDERWATER

Leunig

The Bingo Game.

BABY SHOW TODAY
Leunig

IN THE Sunroom SHE Flicks the BOSSA NOVA button on her organ...

HE goes down to his shed...

...checks his ferret...

opens a can...

and settles down to stare out through his favourite nail hole in the corrugated iron...

CALMLY THEY WAIT AND A QUIET CONFIDENCE SETTLES ACROSS THE LAND.

Stop admiring yourself.

Leunig

oh.... my goodness..
it's so beautiful..

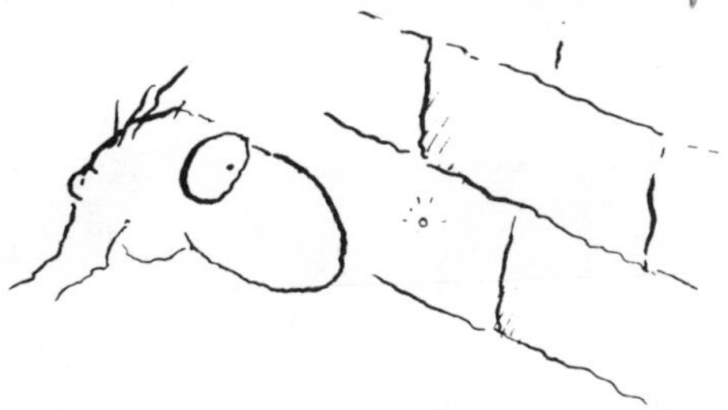

just a tiny piece
of gravel in the brick..
but it's so perfect..

it catches the light...
it glistens.....
it gleams..

I see heavenly
colors...
my head
swims..
my vision
blurrs..

I see the universe...
...everything makes sense..

it's magical...

ACE BARBED WIRE
FACTORY
VIOLETS
40¢
BUNCH
Leunig

On my way to work I was kidnapped by a band of pixies in a hotted up teapot....

I was taken to a large toadstool in the forest I'd read about this sort of thing.... I was about to be de-programmed...

YOU USED TO BELIEVE IN US...
...UNTIL YOU JOINED THAT WEIRD CULT.

relationships
money.
politics
media.
art.
restaurants..
war...
wine...
football...
fashion...
SQUABBLE SQUABBLE SQUABBLE....
WHAT HAPPENED TO YOU ?

YOU USED TO BE SO SWEET...

TO BE CONTINUED ONE DAY...
Leunig

The acoustics could be better? What do you mean, the acoustics could be better? What the hell are you talking about?

Leunig

Footman... come quickly... there's a man sitting on my bed...

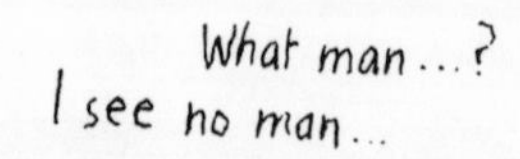
What man...? I see no man...

I AM THE QUEEN...! I COMMAND YOU TO SEE THE MAN ON THE BED.

OHHH.... THAT man on the bed.... of course, of course...

come along my good fellow...

NO... NOT THAT MAN
that's the man who hangs from the chandelier.... I mean the man who sits on the bed.. that man right there...
OH DEAR

DON'T MISS OUT... ORDER NOW... STERLING SILVER SOUVENIR PLATTER.
JULY 1982
MAN ON THE QUEENS BED
Leunig

PHANTOM
Leunig

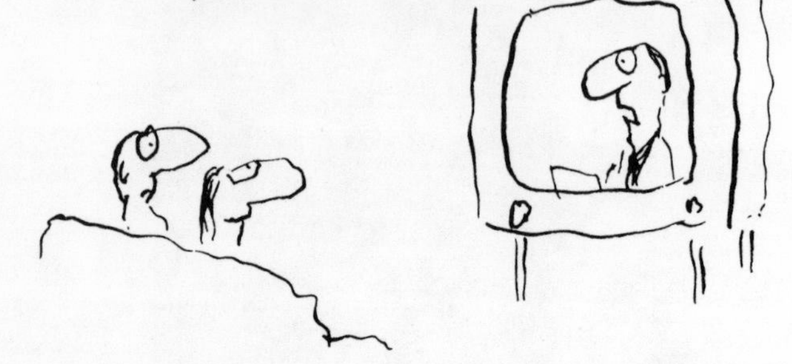
THIS LONELY BRITISH BASTION ... FAR FLUNG FROM ENGLAND'S GREEN AND PEACEFUL PASTURES...

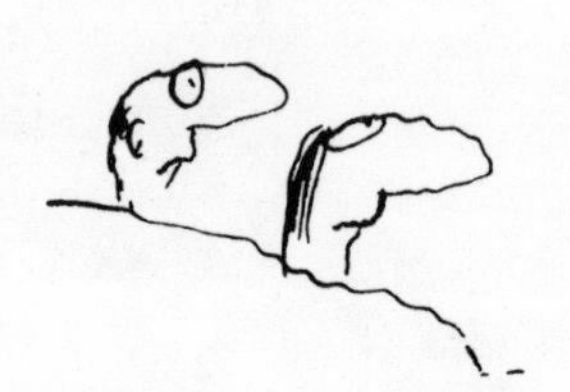

.... SEEMINGLY USELESS BUT SERVING ALWAYS AS A SYMBOL OF BRITISH PLUCK AND DETERMINATION TO STAND AGAINST IMPOSSIBLE ODDS..

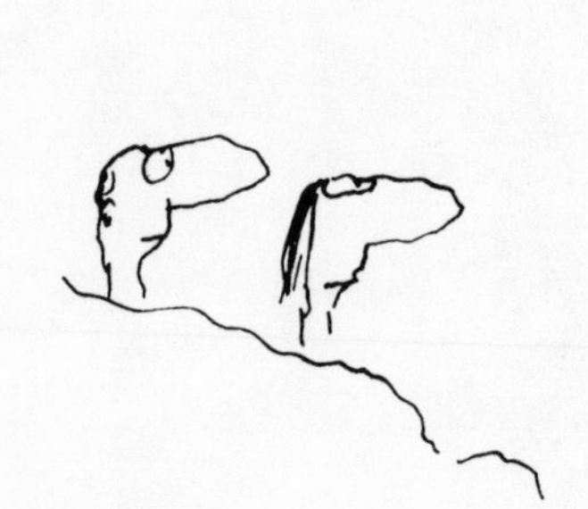

BLEAK, REMOTE AND LONELY... ISOLATED AND DIFFICULT TO DEFEND.

SO MUCH FOR OUR SPECIAL REPORT ON PRINCESS MARGARET...... NOW TO THE FALKLANDS CRISIS...
Leunig

Leunig

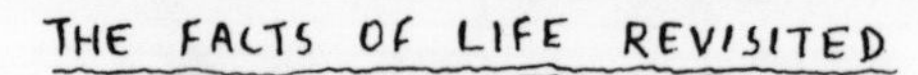

For Princess Diana and Prince Charles the miracle of their first childs' birth approaches..... a miracle of infinite innocence and beauty.

And at Port Stanley Private Dudley Smith awaits another miracle of infinite mystery.

We know where babies come from but where do they go to? Let us marvel. Private Smith is about to be DECONCEIVED

Thousands of small, hot particles are released in a moment of high excitement. Together they surge forward but only one will be successful in its astounding journey.

The chosen particle enters Smith's head and finds its way to his brain and it is here and now that the hallowed miracle of deconception takes place.

In a waiting room in England Smith's father is told the news of the miracle.
He can't think what to call it.
Arrivals and departures...
Commoners and kings...
It's all the same miracle.